The Little
Science thr

From an idea and original work
by the Nursery Staff at
Wyvern Primary School

Additional material by
Sally Featherstone

Illustrations by
Kerry Ingham

Little Books with *BIG*ideas®

The Little Book of Science through Art
ISBN 1 902233 61 1

©Featherstone Education Ltd, 2001, 2005
Text ©Sally Featherstone, 2001
Illustrations ©Kerry Ingham, 2005
Series Editor, Sally Featherstone

First published in the UK, June 2001
Second edition, reillustrated, January 2005

'Little Books' is a trade mark of Featherstone Education Ltd

The right of Sally Featherstone to be identified as the author of this work has been asserted in accordance with Sections 77 and 78 of the Copyright, Designs and Patents Act, 1988.

All rights reserved. No part of this publication may be reproduced by any means, stored in a retrieval system, or transmitted in any form or by any means, electronic, mechanical, photocopying, recording or otherwise, without the prior written consent of the publisher. This book may not be lent, sold, hired out or otherwise disposed of by way of trade in any form of binding or with any cover other than that in which it is published without the prior consent of the publisher, and without this condition being imposed upon the subsequent user.

Published in the United Kingdom by
Featherstone Education Ltd
44 - 46 High Street
Husbands Bosworth
Leicestershire
LE17 6LP

Printed in the UK on paper produced in the European Union from managed, sustainable forests

Contents

Introduction

The activities in this book may not be new to you. Many are already firm favourites in Nursery and Reception classes. What this book does is to identify how art activities can give children in the Foundation Stage opportunities to develop scientific knowledge and concepts.

Learning intentions and concepts

On each page you will find:

- ◆ clearly identified learning intentions from the Early Learning Goals in Knowledge and Understanding of the World

- ◆ scientific concepts which are being established during the activity

- ◆ key vocabulary for the activity (useful for you and for other adults in your team)

- ◆ resources and ingredients needed

- ◆ preparation hints

- ◆ instructions and suggestions for the activity.

We have concentrated in this book on both science and the development of independence. The guidance for preparation involves the children wherever possible. NB Aprons and table covers are needed for all activities. Activities which need close supervision or are 'adult only' are printed in red.

Section I

"Feel It!"

A selection of
tactile materials
to feel, squeeze,
slide, drip, drizzle,
pummel and shape

The Little Book of Science through Art

ELG - investigate objects & materials by using all of their senses.
ELG - look closely at similarities, differences, patterns & change.
Concept - that some materials dissolve when added to water.
Concept - that some substances dissolve quicker than others.
Concept - that water can change when other substances are added.
Concept - that we use our sense of touch to explore the world.

Gloop

Key vocabulary

dissolve	sloppy
thicken	cold
runny	water
air	colour
cornflour	fingers
mix	pattern
sticky	touch
cool	dripping
feel	

Resources & ingredients

- cornflour
- water
- food colouring
- a large container
- a covered table or tray
- aprons

Preparation

1. Mix the water and the colouring into the cornflour.
2. The gloop should have a thick consistency; add extra water if necessary.

The activity

1. Put on aprons.
2. Plunge hands into the gloop and feel the consistency. Use words to describe the feeling: "sticky, slimy, cool," etc.
3. Enjoy exploring the behaviour of gloop as it runs through the fingers, swirls slowly and has a pleasant heavy feeling. Patterns can be made in the air and on the table.

ELG - investigate objects & materials by using all of their senses.
ELG - find out about, & identify some features of objects they observe.
ELG - look closely at differences & change.
Concept - that wet and dry ingredients are mixed to make a dough.
Concept - that heat changes some materials.

Key vocabulary

wet/dry
soft/hard
rough
smooth
mix
liquid
stiff

modelling
stretching
imprint
impressions
smelling
feeling
touching

patting
thumping
poking
pressing
pinching
marking
rolling

Dough

Resources & ingredients

- flour
- salt
- cream of tartar
- cooking oil
- water
- saucepan
- paint or colouring

- aprons
- rolling pins
- cutters
- plastic knives and spatulas
- boards

Preparation

1. **Uncooked dough**
   Mix 2 cups flour, 1 cup salt, 1 tablespoon oil, 1 cup water. Add colouring. Knead till smooth.
2. **Cooked dough**
   In a pan, mix 1 cup flour, 1 cup salt, 4 teaspoons cream of tartar, 2 tablespoons oil, 2 cups water, colouring. Cook for 3 to 5 minutes, stirring until stiff. Cool before use. Store in a bag in the fridge.

The activity

1. Cover the table – and the children!
2. Use dough with cutters, plates, pattern makers, texture tools and rollers.
3. Children like making food with dough, so try giving them several different colours to work with. You can bake and varnish the food for imaginative play; e.g. cakes, vegetables, fruit, animals.
4. Talk to them as they work. Encourage them to experiment with tools and techniques.

ELG - investigate objects & materials by using all of their senses.
ELG - look closely at change.
ELG - ask questions about why things happen & how things work.
Concept - that some materials dissolve when added to water.
Concept - that bubbles will form when soap is added to water, and air is forced in.
Concept - that some substances dissolve quicker than others.
Concept - that water can change when different substances are added.

Slime

Key vocabulary

dissolve	hand
runny	fingers
beat	hold
air	mix
whisk	sticky
slimy	cool
soap	feel
froth	touch

Preparation
1. Dissolve soap flakes in warm water in the container.
2. Add colouring, if desired.
3. Allow mixture to stand until it becomes thick, add more water if necessary.
4. Beat mixture with egg beaters until fluffy.

Resources & ingredients
- Lux soap flakes
- warm water
- food colouring
- egg beaters
- kitchen gadgets
- aprons
- large con-tainer/tray

The activity
1. Put on aprons.
2. Use the kitchen gadgets to pour, beat, scoop and whisk. Encourage the children to use words to describe how the mixture feels and what they are doing.

N.B. Younger children also enjoy slime but need careful supervision to avoid soap getting into their eyes.

The knowledge and concepts (what are they learning?)

ELG - investigate objects & materials by using all of their senses.
ELG - look closely at change in materials.
ELG - ask questions about why things happen & how things work.
Concept - that newspaper is very absorbent.
Concept - that some materials dissolve in water.
Concept - that when the papier mache mixture dries out it becomes hard.

Papier mache

Key vocabulary

wet	change
soggy	squeeze
absorb	paste
dry	sticky
dissolve	tube
hard	
harden	
squash	

Resources & ingredients

- newspapers
- water
- wallpaper paste
- spoon
- a bowl
- card, tape
- scissors
- PVA glue
- fabric/wool

Preparation

1. Help the children to tear the newspapers into small pieces.
2. Mix some wallpaper paste (not too thick!).

The activity

1. Stir the paper pieces into the paste. Talk about the mixture as you take turns to mix.
2. Keep adding paper and stirring until the mixture is stiff enough to mould. Squeeze the mixture with your hands to make sure all the paper is wet.
3. Help the children to make tubes of card to fit one finger and stick with tape.
4. Mould the papier mache round the tube to make a head with nose, eyes and mouth.
5. Put the heads somewhere warm to dry, then paint them, stick on hair, then stick some clothes on with PVA. A big box will make a good theatre.

The Little Book of Science through Art

The knowledge and concepts (what are they learning?)

ELG - investigate objects & materials by using all of their senses.
ELG - look closely at change.
Concept - that clay is soft and malleable when wet.
Concept - that clay is hard and brittle when dry.
Concept - that clay can retain its shape and can be made waterproof.
Concept - that clay can retain impressions.
Concept - that clay's shape can constantly be changed when wet.
Concept - that dry and wet clay are different colours.

Clay

Key vocabulary

wet/dry	imprint	poking
soft/hard	impressions	pressing
rough/smooth	waterproof	pinching
mix	smelling	marking
liquid	feeling	rolling
stiff	touching	
modelling	patting	
stretching	thumping	

Resources & ingredients

- clay
- clay tools
- rolling pins
- cutters
- plastic knives and spatulas
- board
- aprons
- clay cutter
- drying shelf or place

Preparation

1. Talk with the children about working with clay. Make sure they know the group rules for preparation, protection and clearing up.

The activity

1. Cover the table and the children!
2. Many young children will want to explore the clay without making an object. They will just want to experience the feel of it and how they can mould and shape it.
3. As they become more practiced, children may make representations of what they see and do, and may want to keep what they make.
   Talk to them as they work. Encourage them to experiment with tools and techniques, making marks and creating forms and structures.

The knowledge and concepts (what are they learning?)

ELG - investigate objects & materials by using all of their senses.
ELG - find out about, & identify some features of objects and events.
ELG - look closely at change.
ELG - ask questions about why things happen & how things work.
Concept - that substances change when you freeze them.
Concept - that frozen things melt when they get warm.

Ice

Key vocabulary

freeze	liquid	transparent
melt	runny	colour
cold	wet	edges
warm	scratchy	inside
shape	sharp	bubbles
hard	smooth	water
soft	clear	ice

Resources & ingredients

◆ water
◆ ice cube trays and other moulds
◆ freezer
◆ large plastic containers
◆ a glass bowl

Preparation

1. Collect the things you need.
2. Cover the table with plastic to stop drips.
3. You could use a water tray outside.

The activity

1. With the children, fill some of the ice cube trays with clear water.
2. Mix food colouring with water and fill the other trays with different coloured waters.
3. Ask the children what they think will happen when you put the trays in the freezer overnight.
4. Now fill some other moulds with coloured and plain water. Sand moulds, plastic pots, cups, bowls, boxes all make good moulds. Try something large or unusual (such as a wellington, a jelly mould, a rubber glove, an egg box) - anything, as long as you can get it in the freezer!
5. When the water is frozen, feel and look at the coloured ice and talk about what has happened to the coloured cubes.
6. Put the ice into a water tray or other container of water. Watch the ice as it melts. Talk about the big ice moulds and think how they will melt.

Section 2

"What Can My Body Do?"

A selection of ideas which focus on fingers, hands, feet, faces and blown air

Finger Painting

The Little Book of Science through Art

The knowledge and concepts (what are they learning?)

ELG - investigate objects & materials by using all of their senses.
ELG - look closely at similarities, differences, patterns & change.
Concept - that different textures can be made by mixing different ratios of liquid to dry paint.
Concept - that two colours mixed can create a new colour.
Concept - that there is a variety of textures, colours and smells.

Finger painting

Key vocabulary

dissolve
spread
sticky
damp
thick
fluffy
scented
mix

glossy
soft
hard
smooth
lumpy
rough

Resources & ingredients for a range of different paints

- cornflour
- water
- colouring
- glycerine
- starch granules
- flour
- soap flakes
- powder paint
- paste
- scented oils
- sand
- saucepan
- bowl
- mixer
- boards, spoons
- heavy paper

The activity

1. Use a formica topped table or board and aprons.
2. Pour any of the mixtures on a board and get painting! Children love the feeling of the paint.
3. Take time to talk to them as they work.
4. Make prints by covering pictures with paper and peeling off.

Preparation of paints

1. Homemade Paste - mix 1 part flour, 1 part water, colouring.
2. As above, but add 1 part salt.
3. Whipped soap flakes - 2 cups warm water, 1 cup flakes, whisk and add colour. (This mixture can clog drains!!)
4. Cornflour paste - 3 parts water, 1 part cornflour, colouring. Boil water, mix cornflour with a little cold water, add to hot water, stirring all the time. Boil until thick and clear. Add colour.
   Cool before using.
5. You can also paint with non-fungicidal wallpaper paste. Try adding paint, sand or glitter.
* This is a great activity for out of doors!

New Faces

The knowledge and concepts (what are they learning?)

ELG - investigate objects & materials by using all of their senses.
ELG - find out about, & identify some features of living things.
ELG - look closely at similarities and differences.
Concept - that parts of the body have different names.
Concept - that each human being is unique.

Key vocabulary

eyes	nostrils
eyebrows	chin
eyelashes	mouth
ears	tongue
pupils	lips
cheek	teeth
face	reflection
nose	

New faces

Resources & ingredients

- magazines
- card
- lolly sticks
- masking tape
- glue
- scissors
- a mirror

Preparation

1. Help the children to find and cut or tear out face pictures from the magazines.
2. Look for big face pictures or mouths, eyes, etc.
3. Cut some card circles, about the size of a child's face.

The activity

1. Help them to carefully cut round the faces.
2. Talk about the features and compare them with children they can see. Use the mirror to help them compare with their own face.
3. Stick the faces on card circles.
4. Attach a lolly stick to the side or bottom of the card with the tape. (Masking tape is much easier for children to use themselves.)
5. Use the mask to make a new face.
6. Use the mirror to see what a change the mask makes.

Hand and Foot Prints

The Little Book of Science through Art

The knowledge and concepts (what are they learning?)

ELG - investigate objects & materials by using all of their senses.
ELG - find out about, & identify some features of living things.
ELG - look closely at similarities and differences.
Concept - that a print is a reverse replica or reflection of the thing printed.
Concept - that people have left and right feet. That left and right
hands and feet are different and a reverse of each other.

Hand and foot prints

Key vocabulary

footprint	nail
foot	thumb
toe	palm
sole	left
heel	right
hand print	cold
hand	sticky
finger	press

Resources & ingredients

- newspaper
- paint
- shallow bowl or tray for the paint
- paper
- plastic sheet
- a bowl of warm soapy water
- towels

Preparation

1. Put the paint in a shallow bowl.
2. Choose some paper.
3. Put a plastic sheet on the floor.
4. Put a chair in the middle.
5. Help children to take off their shoes and socks.

This activity needs supervision!

The activity

1. The children take turns to sit on the chair.
2. They put their feet into the paint, then stand on a sheet of paper.
3. When they have made their prints by standing or walking on the paper, they step into the warm water to wash their feet.
4. Children can then print with their hands on the same sheet to complete their set of prints.

Paint Blowing

The knowledge and concepts (what are they learning?)

ELG - investigate objects & materials by using all of their senses.
ELG - find out about, & identify some features of objects and events
        they observe.
ELG - ask questions about why things happen & how things work.
Concept - that you can move things without touching them.
Concept - that liquids will flow when you blow or tip the paper.

Paint blowing

Key vocabulary

blow	blob
paper	line
paint	side
move	corner
trickle	edge
run	mix
pour	

Resources & ingredients

◆ runny paint
   or water and
   Edicol
◆ paper

◆ table cover
◆ straws

Preparation

1. Cover the table.
2. Help the children to mix the
   paint or colour.

The activity

1. Explain the activity and ask the children what they think will happen
   when they blow the paint.
2. Pour a small amount of colour onto a sheet of paper.
3. Blow gently and see what happens.
4. Continue the activity by :
        adding another colour
        turning the paper and blowing in a different direction.
5. Try using straws to blow through.
6. Try a collaborative activity - even blowing from different sides of the
   paper.
7. Talk about what happened to the paint when it was blown.

The knowledge and concepts (what are they learning?)

ELG - investigate objects & materials by using all of their senses.
ELG - look closely at change.
ELG - ask questions about why things happen.
Concept - that materials can change when water is added.
Concept - that plaster gives off heat as it dries.

Plaster hand prints

Key vocabulary

wet/dry   feel
soft/hard   stir
rough/smooth   harden
mix   finger
liquid   palm
stiff   thumb
press   print
warm   change

Resources & ingredients

◆ paper or plastic plates
◆ casting plaster
◆ paper clips
◆ powder paint
◆ large ice cream containers
◆ water
◆ spoon

Preparation

1. Pour some plaster into a container.
2. Add some dry powder paint if you wish.
3. Mix in enough water to make a stiff paste.
4. Stir until smooth, but for not too long - it sets quickly!

The activity

1. Cover the table and the children. Roll up sleeves!
2. Put 3 plates out and shape a hanger for each from a paper clip. Put the paper clip on the edge of the plate.
3. The plaster is ready when it holds a finger mark when pressed.
4. Pour some plaster into each plate and smooth the surface.
5. Get the children to place their flat hand into the plaster and remove almost immediately. Talk about what it felt like.
6. Dry overnight. Remove plates and make sure the hanger works.

You could spray the prints gold or silver for a gift for a parent or carer.

Bubble Printing

The knowledge and concepts (what are they learning?)

ELG - investigate objects & materials by using all of their senses.
ELG - find out about, & identify some features of events they observe.
ELG - ask questions about why things happen & how things work.
Concept - that bubbles form when you blow into a liquid.
Concept - that bubbles are light and float.
Concept - that when bubbles burst they leave a wet, circular mark.

Bubble printing

Key vocabulary

bubble	print
blow	pattern
straw	wet/dry
water	circle
liquid	on top
cover	under
paint	squash
shapes	burst

Resources & ingredients

- water
- washing up liquid
- small bowls or margarine pots
- paint or food colouring
- squares of paper
- straws

Preparation

1. Cover the table
2. Help the children to mix some runny paint or water with colouring.
3. Add a few drops of washing up liquid to each pot of colour

The activity

1. Show the children how to blow gently through a straw into the runny paint mixture. Remind them to blow, not suck!
2. Talk to the children about what happens as they blow.
3. When the bubbles have risen above the top of the pot, put a piece of paper over the pot, and remove immediately.
4. The bubbles will leave a pattern on the paper.
5. Leave to dry or repeat with another colour.
   If you paint some cooking oil on the back of the dry pattern, it will become translucent and show the bubbles well.

The Little Book of Science through Art

Section 3

"Paint!"

Exploring paint and what it can do

Mix Your Own Paint

ELG - investigate objects & materials by using all of their senses.
ELG - look closely at similarities, differences, patterns & change.
ELG - ask questions about why things happen & how things work.
Concept - that colours change when they are mixed.
Concept - that mixing the same colours will always result in the same
outcome; e.g. red and yellow make green.

Key vocabulary

mix	add
pour	float
colour	powder
change	brush
swirl	stir

Mix your own paint

Resources & ingredients

- powder or ready mix paint in a range of colours
- paper
- brushes
- spoons
- pans or clear plastic jars

Preparation

1. Cover the surface of a table.
2. Put out a selection of paint colours. Start with three or four.
3. Make sure there are enough spoons and brushes for each mix, or the result will be disappointing.
4. Provide some clean water for brush washing.

The activity

1. This activity is good for children of all ages. Older children could work in pairs.
2. Explain the task to the children, and demonstrate how to mix the colours. Suggest that they try mixing two colours at a time.
3. Help them with the mixing if they need it.
4. Talk with them as they work. Encourage them to watch carefully to see what happens as they mix.
5. Suggest that they try their new colours out on a piece of paper.
6. Keep some of the new colours for a painting session.

The Little Book of Science through Art

The knowledge and concepts (what are they learning?)
ELG - investigate objects & materials by using all of their senses.
ELG - look closely at patterns & change.
ELG - ask questions about why things happen & how things work.
Concept - that some mixtures will harden when exposed to air, because
water evaporates.
Concept - that materials change when you mix them.

Squeezy
bottle painting

Key vocabulary

squeeze	thick
harden	thin
runny	mix
paste	dissolve
dry	
shiny	
glisten	
mixture	

Resources & ingredients

◆ flour
◆ salt
◆ thin paint
◆ table cover
◆ squeezy bottles
◆ thick paper
◆ glitter
◆ funnel

Preparation

1. With the children, mix equal parts of flour and salt.
2. Add thin paint until you get a runny paste.
3. Make several colours if you want.
4. Use the funnel to put the mixture into squeezy bottles.

The activity

1. Cover the table - this is messy!
2. Squeeze the paint onto pieces of thick paper in a trail. Use several colours on a page if they like.
3. Leave to dry. As the pictures dry, the salt will make the paint glisten

A variation
While the painting is still wet, sprinkle glitter over the paint to give it a real sparkle.

Dry Paint Pictures

The knowledge and concepts (what are they learning?)

ELG - investigate objects & materials by using all of their senses.
ELG - look closely at change.
ELG - ask questions about why things happen & how things work.
Concept - that some materials dissolve when they come in contact with a liquid.
Concept - that different coloured paint dissolves at different rates.
Concept - that a liquid can make dry things wet.

Dry paint pictures

Key vocabulary

dry	water
dissolve	cold
stir	powder
mix	float
quicker	starch
slower	spread
runny	
warm	

Resources & ingredients

- dry powder paint
- liquid starch
- brushes
- paint pots
- paper

Preparation

1. Collect all the things you need and talk to the children about wet and dry as you examine each of the things.
2. Cover the table.

The activity

1. Pour a small puddle of starch onto a sheet of paper and spread it out with a brush.
2. With another, slightly damp brush, pick up some dry paint and dab it onto the starch covered paper. The powder will dissolve in the starch and become thick paint. Try using several different colours of paint and talk about the effect. (Some paints will dissolve more quickly than others.)
3. Leave the pictures to dry.

The Little Book of Science through Art

The knowledge and concepts (what are they learning?)

ELG - investigate objects & materials by using all of their senses.
ELG - find out about, & identify some features of objects and events they observe.
ELG - ask questions about why things happen & how things work.
Concept - that paint sticks to things.
Concept - that the roller ball rotates to make marks on the paper.

Key vocabulary

pour	paint
fill	colours
top	roll
ball	hold
track	slide
trail	
pattern	

Roller ball

Resources & ingredients

- old bottles from roller deodorant
- paper
- paint

Preparation

1. With a knife, remove the ball from the top of each bottle. This is an adult activity!
2. Wash the bottles and the balls thoroughly.
3. Help the children to mix some paint (not too thick).

The activity

1. Talk about the roller bottles and how they work.
2. Pour the paint carefully into the bottles and replace the ball in the top of each.
3. Use the bottles to paint patterns or pictures.
4. Talk about how it feels when they draw with the rollers and how the paint gets out of the bottles.
5. Wash the bottles when you have finished and keep them to use again.

The knowledge and concepts (what are they learning?)

ELG - investigate objects & materials by using all of their senses.
ELG - look closely at similarities, differences, patterns & change.
ELG - ask questions about why things happen & how things work.
Concept - that some substances (such as oil) do not dissolve in water.
Concept - that a substance floating on water can be lifted off to make
a print.

Marbling

Key vocabulary

tray	pattern
mix	print
float	lift
oil	wavy
colour	lines
swirl	circles

Resources & ingredients

- a shallow tray or box
- water
- cooking oil
- a dropper
- colouring
- a small jar
- paper
- a stick or spoon
- plastic sheet

Preparation

1. Cover the table.
2. Collect the resources.
3. Help the children to mix some oil with a few drops of colouring in a jar.
4. Cut some paper, smaller than the tray.

The activity

1. Explain the activity and ask the children what they think will happen.
2. Put some water in the tray.
3. Stir the water gently and add a few drops of oil to the surface.
4. The oil will swirl round and float on the water. Watch what happens and talk about it.
5. You can take a print of the pattern by placing a piece of paper gently on the surface and then removing it.
6. You can marble with several colours at once, or wait until one is dry before adding another.
7. When the patterns are dry, coat the back of the paper with a very light film of oil - it will make the colours glow!

The Little Book of Science through Art

The knowledge and concepts (what are they learning?)

ELG - investigate objects & materials by using all of their senses.
ELG - find out about some features of objects and events they observe.
ELG - ask questions about why things happen & how things work.
Concept - that there are many sorts of brushes.
Concept - that brushes can be used in many ways, and that the bristles
on brushes can create spray.

Brush painting

Key vocabulary

paint	bristles
brush	handle
spray	toothbrush
spotty	hairbrush
dotty	washing up brush
splash	paintbrush
stroke	nailbrush
smooth	scrubbing brush

Preparation

1. Collect together as many brushes as you can. Ask children to bring old brushes from home, or go to the local shops to see what you can find.
2. Choose some strong paper to work on.
3. Mix the paint.

Resources & ingredients

◆ paint
◆ paper
◆ sticks or rulers

◆ brushes - e.g. paint, pastry, hair, nail, tooth, washing up, shoe polish, blusher, dustpan, decorating

The activity

1. Talk about the different sorts and their uses. Compare bristles by touch. Talk about the length and size of bristles, the different handles.
2. Dip the brushes in the paint and use them to print and paint.
3. Talk about the different marks.
4. Now try using a stick or ruler to spray paint by passing the stick across the bristles.
   <u>Always pull the stick towards you or you will get sprayed!!</u>
5. Talk about what happens.

The Little Book of Science through Art

The knowledge and concepts (what are they learning?)

ELG - investigate objects & materials by using all of their senses.
ELG - find out about, & identify some features of objects they observe.
ELG - look closely at patterns & change.
ELG - ask questions about why things happen & how things work.
Concept - that wax and water do not mix.
Concept - that wax protects paper from paint.

Candle painting

Key vocabulary

wax
invisible
see
feel
slippery
draw
paint

brush
thin
show
white
disappear
appear

Preparation

1. Help the children to mix the paint.
2. Find some candles and big crayons.
3. Cover the table.
4. Cut some different sizes and colours of paper. White paper works well with candles or crayons.

Resources & ingredients

- white candles
- crayons
- thin paint, Brusho or Edicol
- big brushes
- smooth coloured paper

The activity

1. Explain the activity and ask the children what they think will happen and why.
2. Draw pictures and patterns with the candles on the paper. Encourage the children to press hard with the candle, so plenty of wax gets onto the paper.
3. Brush thin paint all over the paper to reveal the pattern or picture.
4. You can use crayons on white paper to get similar effects.
5. Talk about what happens as you work.

The Little Book of Science through Art

Section 4

"Print It!"

A selection of ideas for making printed pictures and patterns

The Little Book of Science through Art

The knowledge and concepts (what are they learning?)

ELG - investigate objects & materials by using all of their senses.
ELG - find out about, & identify some features of objects they observe.
ELG - ask questions about why things happen & how things work.
Concept - that sponges soak up and hold water and paint.
Concept - that squeezing or pressing will release the paint from a sponge.

Sponge Printing

Key vocabulary

sponge	bubbles
paint	dip
soak	mark
squeeze	overlap
press	smooth
print	bumpy
holes	rough

Resources & ingredients

- sponge pieces from packing
- baby sponges
- kitchen sponges
- bath sponge
- natural sponges
- scissors
- paint
- paper

Preparation

1. Find a range of sorts of sponges.
2. Help the children to mix some thickish paint and pour into saucers or polystyrene trays.
3. Cut some paper in different colours, shapes and sizes.
4. Cover the table.

The activity

1. Look at, feel and talk about the different sorts of sponges, their textures and their uses.
2. Cut some of the sponges into simple shapes - circles, stars, triangles, etc.
3. Dip the sponge pieces into the paint and press them onto the paper.
4. Lift each piece off carefully. Talk about the patterns the different sponges make.
5. Sponge printing is an effective texture for the background of big pictures or painting on windows. Use it for grass, sea, clouds, sky, etc.

52

The knowledge and concepts (what are they learning?)

ELG - investigate objects & materials by using all of their senses.
ELG - look closely at similarities, differences, patterns & change.
ELG - find out about, & identify some features of things they observe.
ELG - ask questions about why things happen & how things work.
Concept - that patterns can be made with natural materials.
Concept - that fruit and vegetables have symmetry and pattern.

Fruit & veg printing

Key vocabulary

fruit/veg names,	press
colours & shapes	pattern
core	paint
pip	next
skin	again
peel	smooth
stalk	bumpy
leaf	shiny
juice	

Resources & ingredients

- fruit (try apples, oranges, lemons, star fruit, pears - avoid very soft fruit)
- vegetables (try potatoes, carrots, tomatoes, onions, cucumber)
- old forks
- knife
- cutting board
- paper
- thickish paints in shallow trays
- paint brushes or sponges

Preparation

1. Help the children to cut the fruit and vegetables in half.
2. Stick a fork in some of the pieces to make them easier to hold.
3. Mix the paint and put some paper ready.

The activity

1. Either dip the fruit and vegetables in the paint or paint the flat surface.
2. Press onto the paper and lift off carefully to reveal the print.
3. Repeat with different fruit and vegetables to make a pattern.
4. Try making a repeating pattern of different colours or shapes, such as lemon, apple, lemon, apple.
5. You could try printing on some fabric or on card to make a greeting card, or make wrapping paper or curtains for the home corner .

The Little Book of Science through Art

53

The Little Book of Science through Art

The knowledge and concepts (what are they learning?)

The knowledge and concepts (what are they learning?)

ELG - investigate objects & materials by using all of their senses.

ELG - look closely at patterns & change.

Concept - that a print reverses the original.

Concept - that paint patterns on folded paper will produce a mirror or symmetrical image.

Concept - that string and wool absorb liquids.

String prints

Key vocabulary

cut	marks
dip	fold
string	press
wet	pull
drippy	carefully
colour	unfold
wiggly	pattern
drops	same

Resources & ingredients

- string or wool
- paper
- scissors
- fairly thick paint in saucers, plates or bowls

Preparation

1. Collect the things you need.
2. Help the children to cut some wool or string into lengths.
3. Cut some paper and help the children to fold each piece of paper in half.

The activity (this will need help)

1. Put a piece of paper (flattened out) on the table.
2. Help them to choose a piece of string or wool and a paint colour.
3. Put the string into the paint, leaving one end out of the paint.
4. Lift the string out of the paint and put it on one half of the paper with the clean end off the edge of the paper.
5. Fold the paper carefully in half over the string.
6. Smooth the paper all over.
7. Put a hand on top of the paper and gently pull the string out.
8. Unfold the paper to reveal a symmetrical pattern!
9. Talk about what has happened.

The knowledge and concepts (what are they learning?)
ELG - investigate objects & materials by using all of their senses.
ELG - ask questions about why things happen & how things work.
Concept - that printing leaves the pattern of an object.
Concept - that different materials make different printed patterns.

Key vocabulary

mesh	pattern
tights	paint
soak	same
fasten	squeeze
elastic band	print
cotton wool	

Mesh pad printing

Preparation

1. Cover the table.
2. Help the children to mix some thickish paint in several colours. Pour the paint into saucers or trays
3. Cut some squares of different sorts of net.
4. Cut some paper in different shapes and colours.

Resources & ingredients

- nets from fruit and vegetables, old tights, net curtain, etc.
- scissors
- cotton wool
- elastic bands
- paint

The activity

1. Feel the different sorts of net, talk about their uses and the purposes of net.
2. Talk about the sorts of patterns they might make.
3. Help the children to wrap net pieces round the cotton wool and fasten them with an elastic band or a peg.
4. Dip the pads in paint and print with them on the paper.
5. Talk about what happens and the different prints made by different sorts of nets.
6. Display the pictures with some examples of the nets you used to print them with.

The Little Book of Science through Art

Section 5

"Feel It!"

Some activities for outside

ELG - investigate objects & materials by using all of their senses.
ELG - find out about, & identify some features of living things and objects.
ELG - look closely at similarities, differences, patterns.
Concept - that there is pattern in nature.
Concept - that when we rub a textured surface through paper, with a
        crayon, we get an identical pattern (cause and effect).

Texture rubbing

Key vocabulary

rough	lines
bark	spots
shells	bumpy
pattern	lumps
natural	rub
smooth	colour
leaves	wavy
stones	slippery
hard	
soft	

Resources & ingredients

- shells
- bark
- stones
- leaves
- ribbon, etc.

- crayons
- paper
- scissors
- magnifying glass

Preparation

1. With the children, collect some objects with surface texture. Try feeling with closed eyes.
2. You could stick some things, such as ribbon, braid, silver paper, lace on card before rubbing.

The activity

1. Look and feel the textures and patterns of the surfaces outside and inside the room. Talk about the textures.
2. Lay the paper on the objects and rub over the paper with crayon. (Thick crayons, used on their sides work best). Try using several colours on the same piece of paper.
3. Talk about the patterns as they appear.

A variation

Use a white candle instead of a crayon to do the rubbing. Then wash over with very thin water based paint such as Edicol.

Wet Sand

The Little Book of Science through Art

The knowledge and concepts (what are they learning?)

ELG - investigate objects & materials by using all of their senses.
ELG - look closely at similarities, differences, patterns & change.
ELG - ask questions about why things happen & how things work.
Concept - that wet and dry sand feel and behave differently.
Concept - that you can make patterns in wet sand.
Concept - that you can mould and shape wet sand more easily than dry sand.

Wet sand

Key vocabulary

wet	castle
dry	mark
pattern	lines
mould	wavy
spade	straight
bucket	grains
spoon	pour

Resources & ingredients

- dry sand
- a tray or container
- water
- sand moulds
- spades
- spoons
- scoops
- sticks
- buckets

Preparation

1. Collect all the equipment you need.
2. Put dry sand in a flat container or the sand tray.

The activity

1. Talk with the children about the feel of dry sand and how it behaves, pouring, sieving, scooping and shaping it.
2. Help the children to add a small amount of water and mix it in.
3. Talk about how the sand changes as it gets wet. Can you do the same things with wet sand? Can you pour it, sieve it, scoop it? Is it easier or more difficult to shape and mould?
4. Use the moulds, sticks, forks, scoops and buckets to make sand pies, cakes, castles. Talk about the feel of the wet sand.
5. Try adding more water, a little at a time, watching what happens until the sand is really runny. Keep talking about what happens.

The Little Book of Science through Art

The knowledge and concepts (what are they learning?)

ELG - investigate objects & materials by using all of their senses.
ELG - find out about, & identify some features of objects and events they observe.
ELG - ask questions about why things happen & how things work.
Concept - that water flows downhill.
Concept - that water will carry objects and some will float.

Water chute

Key vocabulary

water	bottom
down	end
splash	fast
float	slow
sink	slope
pour	wheel
pipe	bridge
top	canal

Resources & ingredients

- plastic drain pipe or gutter
- water
- plastic sheet
- big bricks
- plastic jugs and bottles
- bucket/tray for the bottom
- boats to float

Preparation

This is a good activity for out of doors!

1. Put down a plastic sheet.
2. Collect the other things you need.

The activity

1. Show the children the equipment and talk about how you could build water chutes and slides.
2. Let them work out how to do it. Offer help if they get stuck.
3. Talk about what happens.
4. Introduce the idea of floating boats or other things down the chutes. Talk about the difference in speed and splash of different slopes.
5. Try joining lengths of guttering to make a long waterway for floating boats or ducks. Incorporate tubes and pipes. Try water wheels and gates to stop the flow. Use bricks to prop up bridges.
6. Make the system go under and over things, outdoors and indoors.

The Little Book of Science through Art

Section 6

"Light and Dark"

Ideas for exploring light and shadow

The Little Book of Science through Art

The knowledge and concepts (what are they learning?)

ELG - investigate objects & materials by using all of their senses.
ELG - look closely at similarities, differences, patterns & change.
ELG - ask questions about why things happen & how things work.
Concept - that painting on glass can produce a transparent picture.
Concept - that the picture will be reversed when seen from the other side of the window.
Concept - that you can paint on different surfaces.

Window painting

Key vocabulary

mix	sunlight
paint	back to front
colour	outside
transparent	inside
through	different
wet/dry	waterproof

Preparation

1. Talk to the children and get their suggestions for subjects for a window painting.
2. Plan where the picture will go and whether it be on the inside or the outside.
3. Mix some washing up liquid or PVA into the paint. PVA lasts longer.

Resources & ingredients

- white paint
- coloured paint
- washing up liquid
- brushes
- newspaper or plastic sheeting
- PVA glue

The activity

1. Cover the floor or ground below the window.
2. Help the children to paint the outlines of the picture in white paint with finer brushes.
3. Encourage them to stand back and look at the picture as they work.
4. Go to the other side of the window and look from there. Talk about what you see.
5. When the children are happy with the outlines, help them to fill in the painting. Then look from inside and out, in sun and rain.
6. PVA makes the paint transparent and waterproof, <u>but it is harder to remove!</u>

The Little Book of Science through Art

The knowledge and concepts (what are they learning?)

ELG - investigate objects & materials by using all of their senses.
ELG - find out about, & identify some features of objects and events they observe.
ELG - ask questions about why things happen & how things work.
Concept - that objects cast shadows.
Concept - that lights and sunlight make shadows appear.

Shadow puppets

Key vocabulary

card	shine
shape	move
puppet	screen
stick	behind
shadow	in front
light	audience

Resources & ingredients

- card
- sticks
- crayons or paint
- scissors
- masking tape
- a torch or projector
- a screen, or fabric on a frame

Preparation

1. Collect the things you need.
2. Make the screen and set up the light source.
3. Involve the children in setting up the screen and light. Cotton sheeting on a batten or pole will work just as well for a screen.

The activity

1. Before you make the puppets, let the children experiment with the light source and screen, talking about what happens and how shadows are made.
2. When you are ready, show the children how to make a shadow puppet by drawing a shape and fixing it on a stick.
3. Help them to make and colour their own puppets. You could make the characters from favourite stories or poems.
4. Now let the children experiment with their puppets. Talk about what happens.
5. They could have a puppet show. You could invite their parents or children from another class or group.

Collage on Transparent Surfaces

The Little Book of Science through Art

The knowledge and concepts (what are they learning?)

ELG - investigate objects & materials by using all of their senses.
ELG - find out about, & identify some features of objects they observe.
ELG - ask questions about why things happen & how things work.
Concept - that some materials are transparent or translucent.
Concept - that light passes through transparent materials and colours
are projected by the light.

Collage on transparent surfaces

Key vocabulary

transparent	stick
see through	scissors
paper	hang
cellophane	ceiling
colour	show
shine	different
sunlight	through
cut	reflection

Resources & ingredients

- pieces of clear plastic or cellophane
- coloured cellophane
- sweet & other wrappers
- scissors
- white glue
- a stick or string for hanging

Preparation

1. Help the children to collect transparent materials at home and school. It may take several days.
2. Talk about the things and look through them.
3. Collect the other things you need.
4. Cover the table.

The activity

1. Before you start, let the children explore the papers by holding them up to their eyes, to the window or to a torch.
2. Cut some strips of clear plastic or cellophane.
3. Children can now cut and stick their own pieces of transparent materials to make a hanging.
4. Hang the collages on strings or sticks, where light or sunlight will shine though them.
5. Talk about what happens when the light shines through the collages.

The Little Book of Science through Art

73

If you have found this book useful you might also like ...

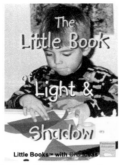

The Little Book of
Light & Shadow
LB25
ISBN 1-904187-81-1

The Little Book of
Investigations
LB20
ISBN 1-904187-66-8

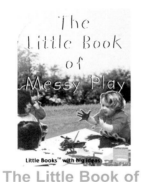

The Little Book of
Messy Play
LB13
ISBN 1-904187-09-9

The Little Book of
Cooking From Stories
LB7
ISBN 1-904187-04-8

All available from

Featherstone Education   PO Box 6350
Lutterworth LE17 6ZA

T:0185 888 1212   F:0185 888 1360

on our web site

www.featherstone.uk.com

and from selected
book suppliers